The 20-Minute

Bible
Study
Workbook

The 20-Minute
Bible
Study
Workbook

Volume 4 – 13 Weeks

Luke, Acts, 1 John, 2 Peter, James

J. A. Marucci
R. K. Brownrigg

Happy Tent Media Group

INTRODUCTION

This Bible study workbook has been carefully designed and refined over many years to help you effectively learn what the Bible says. The workbook is set up for Monday through Saturday use, and a day's reading and answering questions will usually take about 20 minutes. It is primarily designed for personal study but can be adapted for small group use.

Try to set aside the same time each day. If you are a morning person, try to do this first thing. Not everyone is a morning person, and many people prefer later in the day, evening, or during a lunch break. Whenever the best time of day is for you, try to set aside the same time daily.

To get the most out of this workbook, you will want to read the daily assigned reading and write down your answers to the questions presented. You can write in the workbook, as there is space under each question to write down answers.

It is normal to miss a time or two for various reasons. Don't let missing discourage you from picking it back up. If you miss a day or even a week, start again with the next day's reading or the beginning of the following week.

Finally, your positive rating and a written review of this workbook will make it more readily available for others to find and use. If you find this workbook helpful, please consider taking a moment and posting a review on Amazon.com.

Thank you, and God bless you as you study the Bible!

J. A. Marucci
R. K. Brownrigg

Name:_____ Date Started: _____

Weekly Checklist/Contents:

"...be attentive to my words; incline your ear to my sayings. Let them not escape from your sight; keep them within your heart. For they are life to those who find them, and healing to all their flesh." — Proverbs 4:20-22 (ESV)

Week 1 — This week's Bible reading will begin our walk through the Gospel of Luke. We'll look at the birth of John the Baptist, the birth of Jesus, Jesus consecrated as a baby at the temple, and Jesus at the temple at the age of twelve.

Monday

Read Luke 1:1–25

What does this passage tell us about Zechariah and his wife, Elizabeth? (Luke 1:5–7)

What did Gabriel tell Zechariah about what his son John would be like and what he would do? (Luke 1:14–17).

How did Zechariah respond to the message from Gabriel? What happened to him because of his response? (Luke 1:18–22)

Read Luke 1:26–56

What specifically did the angel Gabriel tell Mary? What was said about the rule and reign of Jesus? (Luke 1:28–33)

How did Mary react to the message that Gabriel brought to her? How did Gabriel answer her question? How did Mary reply to Gabriel? (Luke 1:34–38)

Summarize Mary's song focusing on what God had done (look at the words "He" and "His"). (Luke 1:46–55)

Wednesday

Read Luke 1:57–80

How was Zechariah's speech restored to him? What was the result of this event on the people of the region? (Luke 1:57–66)

What did Zechariah praise God for in the first part of his prophecy? (Luke 1:67–75)

What did Zechariah prophesy concerning his son John? (Luke 1:76–79)

Read Luke 2:1–21

What were the circumstances surrounding Jesus' birth? (Luke 2:1–7)

How did God reveal the birth of Jesus to the shepherds? What exactly did the angel of the Lord say to the shepherds? (Luke 2:9–12)

What did the shepherds do in response to the angelic visitation? (Luke 2:15–20)

Read Luke 2:22–40

Who was Simeon? What had God promised to do for him before he died? What did he say about Jesus? (Luke 2:25–32)

What else did Simeon say to Mary about Jesus? (Luke 2:34–35)

Who was Anna? What was her part in the story? (Luke 2:36–38)

Read Luke 2:41–52

Where did they find Jesus after searching for him for three days? What was He doing when they found Him? How did his parents react when they found him? (Luke 2:46–48)

What did Jesus say to his parents after He was found at the temple? (Luke 2:49–50)

What does the rest of this passage tell us about Jesus' life as a young man? (Luke 2:51–52)

Week 2 — This week's Bible reading will continue our walk through the Gospel of Luke. We'll look at the ministry of John the Baptist, the start of Jesus' ministry, Jesus calling Simon, Jesus healing on the Sabbath, the Centurion's faith, and the Parable of the Sower.

Monday

Read Luke 3

What did John proclaim? What did Isaiah the prophet write concerning who John was? (Luke 3:2–6)

How did John respond when the people were wondering if he might be the Christ? (Luke 3:15–17)

What events surrounded Jesus' baptism? How old was Jesus when He began His ministry? (Luke 3:21–23)

Read Luke 4

What scripture did Jesus use to announce His ministry and what were the main elements outlined? (Luke 4:17–19)

How did the people of Jesus' hometown initially respond to Him? How did they later respond? What caused this change of attitude toward Jesus? (Luke 4:22–30)

In this passage how did Jesus deliver the man with an unclean demon? How did Jesus heal Simon's mother-in-law? How did Jesus heal those with various diseases? (Luke 4:33–41)

Read Luke 5

What did Jesus tell Simon to do? How did Simon react and what happened as a result? What new profession did Jesus give to Simon and how did he and the others respond? (Luke 5:4–11)

Who came to Jesus and fell with his face to the ground? What did he say to Jesus and how did Jesus respond? What resulted from this? (Luke 5:12–16)

Who was brought to Jesus for healing and how? Whose faith did Jesus respond to and what did He proclaim? How did the Pharisees and the teachers of the law react to Jesus' proclamation over the man and why? How did Jesus heal the man? (Luke 5:17–26)

Read Luke 6

What was the setting of this healing? What were the Pharisees and teachers of the law looking for? How did Jesus respond to this situation? (Luke 6:6–11)

What did Jesus say to do in this passage specifically toward those who hate, curse and abuse us? How are we told to treat our enemies? What reward is there for us in doing this? (Luke 6:27–29, 35–36)

What did Jesus say about giving in this verse? (Luke 6:38)

Read Luke 7

Why did the centurion send the Jewish elders to Jesus? How did Jesus respond to their plea for help? Why did Jesus declare that the centurion had great faith? (Luke 7:1–10)

What was happening as Jesus and the crowd approached the town gate of Nain? What was Jesus' initial reaction to this sad situation? What did He do about it and how did the people react? (Luke 7:11–17)

How did the Pharisee react to the sinful woman touching Jesus' feet? What story does Jesus tell to exemplify forgiveness? What did He tell the woman? (Luke 7:36–50)

Read Luke 8:1–25

What do we learn about the women who followed Jesus and traveled with Him and His disciples? (Luke 8:1–3)

What is the seed in this parable? Who do those along the path, rock, thorns, and good soil represent? What are the thorns Jesus mentioned and their effect on the seed? (Luke 8:11–15).

Summarize the story of Jesus calming the storm. (Luke 8:22–25)

Week 3 — This week's Bible reading will continue our walk through the Gospel of Luke. We'll look at Jesus' healing ministry, Jesus sending twelve and the seventy-two, the transfiguration, the Parable of the Good Samaritan, and Jesus teaching on prayer.

Monday

Read Luke 8:26–56

What was the condition of the demon-possessed man? How did he react when first seeing Jesus? How did the people react to the man being set free and what did they ask of Jesus? (Luke 8:26–29, 34–37)

What was the state of the woman in these verses, what did she do and what happened to her? How did Jesus know that someone had touched Him while in the midst of the crowd? (Luke 8:43–48)

What did Jesus say to Jairus when they both heard the news of his daughter's death? How did Jesus raise the little girl from the dead? (Luke 8:49–56)

Read Luke 9:1–17

What are we told Jesus gave the twelve and why did He send them out? What were the results of their mission? (Luke 9:1–6)

What happened when the disciples returned from their mission? How did Jesus react to the crowds that followed Him? (Luke 9:10–11)

What did the twelve suggest concerning the crowds that were present? What was Jesus' solution to the problem facing them? What did Jesus do to fix the problem? (Luke 9:12–17)

Read Luke 9:18–62

What happened when Jesus was praying on the mountain? Who appeared and talked with Jesus? What did the voice from the cloud say? (Luke 9:28–36)

What are we told was the cause of this boy's seizures? How did Jesus restore the boy? (Luke 9:37–43)

How does Jesus reply to the three people who wanted to follow Him? (Luke 9:57–62)

Read Luke 10

What did Jesus tell the seventy-two to do when He sent them out? (Luke 10:4–11)

What happened upon the return of the seventy-two? What was Jesus' take on their mission and how did He frame their success in light of eternity? (Luke 10:17–20)

How does Jesus define loving one's neighbor? (Luke 10:25–37)

Friday

Read Luke 11

What situation does Jesus use to teach on prayer? What causes the man to rise and give his friend what he needs? What is Jesus teaching us about prayer by using this example? (Luke 11:5–10)

What were the first three woes that Jesus gave to the Pharisees? (Luke 11:37–44)

What were the three woes that Jesus spoke to the lawyers? How did Jesus' woes spoken against the Pharisees and the teachers of the law affect their attitude toward Jesus? (Luke 11:45–54)

Read Luke 12:1–34

Who does Jesus tell us not to fear and why? Who does He tell us to fear? What encouragements does Jesus provide us with in this passage? What else does Jesus say concerning acknowledging Him or disowning Him before men? (Luke 12:4–9)

What does Jesus say about covetousness? In the story of the rich farmer, what did Jesus teach about storing up possessions for oneself? (Luke 12:13–21)

What does Jesus use as illustrations to teach us not to worry about our needs being met? Why should these two examples encourage our trust in God's ability and willingness to provide for us? What does Jesus say in summary about our worrying about our needs being met? (Luke 12:22–31)

Week 4 — This week's Bible reading will continue our walk through the Gospel of Luke. We'll look at Jesus healing on the Sabbath, the Parable of the Lost Son, the rich man and Lazarus, the healing of the ten lepers, and Jesus teaching on end times.

Monday

Read Luke 12:35–59

What does Jesus say to do in these verses? What reward is there for those who keep ready watching? (Luke 12:35–40)

What sober warnings are given in these verses? What specifically does Jesus say concerning being accountable for what we've been entrusted? (Luke 12:45–48)

What does Jesus say to those who think He will bring peace on the earth? (Luke 12:49–53)

Read Luke 13

What was Jesus communicating in His response to those who had told Him about the Galileans who had suffered under Pilate, and concerning those who died when the tower in Siloam fell on them? (Luke 13:1–5)

What do we learn about the woman that Jesus healed? What did Jesus say and do concerning the woman? How did the synagogue ruler react to this healing? What example did Jesus use to rebuff the synagogue ruler? (Luke 13:10–17)

How did Jesus answer the person who asked if only a few people would be saved? What story did He use to illustrate this? (Luke 13:22–27)

Read Luke 14

In this passage, what are we told that Jesus did? To what did He equate healing the man on the Sabbath? (Luke 14:1–6)

What were the main points that Jesus made in the Parable of the great banquet? (Luke 14:16–24)

According to this passage, what things does Jesus say will prohibit a person from being able to be His disciple? What two examples does Jesus use to illustrate counting the cost of following Him? (Luke 14:25–33).

Read Luke 15

What is said about the son's condition when he came to his senses? What did the son say to himself? (Luke 15:14–19)

What was the father's attitude toward the wayward son returning home? What specifically did the father do when the son returned? (Luke 15:20–24)

What was the older brother's reaction? (Luke 15:25–31)

Read Luke 16

What does Jesus say about faithfulness and dishonesty? (Luke 16:10–12)

What does Jesus say about serving two masters? How did the Pharisees respond to this teaching and why? What else does Jesus tell us in these verses? (Luke 16:13–15)

What are we told about the state of the rich man and Lazarus during their lifetimes and after death? What does Abraham tell the rich man that prohibits Lazarus from helping him? What is the final thing Abraham tells the rich man? (Luke 16:19–31)

Read Luke 17

What example did Jesus use to describe the role of a servant? What actions and attitude does Jesus expect of us as servants? (Luke 17:7–10)

Who came to Jesus while He was traveling along the border of Samaria and Galilee? What did these men ask of Jesus? What did Jesus tell them to do and what happened to them? (Luke 17:11–19)

What two time periods does Jesus use to illustrate what it will be like in the days before His return? What do these tell us about the time before Jesus returns? (Luke 17:26–30)

Week 5 — This week's Bible reading will continue our walk through the Gospel of Luke. We'll look at the Parable of the Persistent Widow, the blind beggar, Zacchaeus, the Parable of the Ten Minas, the triumphal entry, and the Parable of the Talents.

Monday

Read Luke 18:1–17

Why did Jesus teach the disciples this parable? What were the characteristics of the judge and the widow? Why did the judge give in to the widow's plea? What does Jesus tell us about God's willingness to answer persistent prayer? (Luke 18:1–8)

How did the Pharisee and tax collector pray? What was Jesus' take on these two examples of prayer? (Luke 18:9–14)

How did the disciples react to people bringing babies to Jesus? How did Jesus react and what did He say about how we need to receive the kingdom of God? (Luke 18:15–17)

Read Luke 18:18–43

What did the rich ruler ask Jesus? How did Jesus answer him? What did the ruler lack and what did Jesus promise him in this regard? (Luke 18:18–22)

How did the rich ruler respond to Jesus' counsel? What sober truth did Jesus give concerning rich people? What perspective did Jesus give His disciples concerning their commitment to Him? (Luke 18:23–30)

Who called out to Jesus as He approached Jericho? How did those in front respond to the man? How did Jesus interact with the man? What was the result of this interaction? (Luke 18:35–43)

Read Luke 19

Who was Zacchaeus and what did he do in order to see Jesus? How did Jesus respond to Zacchaeus? What did Zacchaeus do that showed his repentance? What do we learn about Jesus' mission? (Luke 19:1–10)

What did the servants do with their master's money and how did the master react to each? (Luke 19:11–27)

How did the crowd of disciples react to Jesus as He rode the colt toward Jerusalem? What did the Pharisees complain to Jesus concerning? What did Jesus say to them? (Luke 19:36–40)

Read Luke 20

Who did the owner of the vineyard send to the tenants at harvest time and how was each treated? (Luke 20:9–16)

How did the spies sent to Jesus attempt to catch Him in something He said? How did Jesus answer their trick question? What truth can we glean from this interchange? (Luke 20:20–26)

What far-fetched story did the Sadducees come up with to test Jesus? What do we learn from Jesus' reply? (Luke 20:27–40)

Friday

Read Luke 21

What did Jesus warn the disciples to watch out for? What are some of the things that Jesus said will happen before the end comes? (Luke 21:5–11)

What did Jesus say will happen to those who believe during this time? How would you describe these times for those who believe? (Luke 21:12–19)

What else did Jesus say would characterize this time? What warnings and counsel does Jesus provide? (Luke 21:25–28, 34–36)

Read Luke 22:1–38

What do we learn about the desires of the chief priests and the teachers of the law? What are we told about Judas and what he did? How did the chief priests and the officers react to Judas' offer? (Luke 22:1–6)

What specifically did Jesus say about the bread and the cup? (Luke 22:17–20)

What did Jesus say about the way authority is exercised in this world? How did He say believers are to act in contrast? (Luke 22:24–26)

Week 6 — This week's Bible reading will conclude our walk through the Gospel of Luke. We will look at Jesus' betrayal and arrest, Jesus before Pilate, Jesus' crucifixion, death and burial, and Jesus' resurrection.

Monday

Read Luke 22:39–71

What did Jesus pray? What are we told about the intensity of His prayer? Why were the disciples asleep? (Luke 22:39–46)

How did Judas single out Jesus to the crowd? What did Jesus' followers do in response to what was going to happen? (Luke 22:47–51)

How did the men who were guarding Jesus treat him? How did Jesus answer the question about being the Christ and about being the Son of God? (Luke 22:63–71)

Read Luke 23:1–25

What did they accuse Jesus of before Pilate? How did Jesus answer Pilate when asked if He were the king of the Jews? How did Pilate react to this? (Luke 23:1–4)

Why was Herod pleased to see Jesus? How did Jesus respond to Herod's questions? How did the chief priests and scribes, and Herod and his soldiers treat Jesus? (Luke 23:8–11)

What did Pilate state plainly about Jesus to the chief priests, rulers, and the people? How did they react to Pilate's statement? What are we told Pilate did in response to the insistent shouts of the crowd? (Luke 23:13–25)

Read Luke 23:26–56

How did the rulers, soldiers, and the two criminals respond to Jesus on the cross? (Luke 23:32–43)

What does it say happened beginning at the sixth hour? What did Jesus say upon His death? How did the Centurion react? (Luke 23:44–47)

What are we told about the man who asked Pilate for Jesus' body? Where did he bury Jesus? Who else witnessed Jesus being buried? (Luke 23:50–56)

Read Luke 24:1–12

What did the women who went to the tomb early on the first morning find when they arrived there? Who appeared to those who had come to the tomb and how did they react to this visitation? (Luke 24:1–5)

What did the men in dazzling apparel tell the women about Jesus? (Luke 24:6–7)

How did the apostles respond to the news from the women? What did Peter do? (Luke 24:9–12)

Read Luke 24:13–35

Who joined the two who were walking to Emmaus that were discussing what had happened? How did these two respond to being questioned? (Luke 24:13–18)

How did the two men describe Jesus? What else did they explain about recent events? (Luke 24:19–24)

What did Jesus say to these two, what did He explain to them, and how did He reveal Himself to them? What did they do after this? (Luke 24:25–35)

Saturday

Read Luke 24:36–53

How did Jesus appear to the disciples? How did they react? What else did He do to prove to them that He was alive? (Luke 24:36–43)

What are we told that Jesus did for those present? What specifically did He tell them would happen? Why did He tell them to stay in the city? (Luke 24:45–49)

What does this passage tell us about Jesus' ascension? What do we learn about what the disciples did after this? (Luke 24:50–53)

Week 7 — This week's Bible reading will begin our walk through the book of Acts. We will learn what the early Church did together, what happened at Pentecost, how they were empowered and grew, and how they were persecuted by the religious establishment.

Monday

Read Acts 1

What is one of the primary purposes of the power of the Holy Spirit in the life of the believer? (Acts 1:8)

What do we learn about how Jesus will return to the earth someday? (Acts 1:9–11)

What did the early believers do prior to the day of Pentecost in Chapter 2? (Acts 1:14)

Read Acts 2

Explain what happened to the disciples then through the disciples when the day of Pentecost arrived. (Acts 2:1–13)

List the things that will occur in the Last Days. According to this passage, who can be saved? (Acts 2:17–21)

What did the new believers commit themselves to? What else happened? (Acts 2:42–47).

Wednesday

Read Acts 3

Why were Peter and John going to the temple? What was the condition of the man and how did he respond to seeing Peter and John? What did Peter say to the man? (Acts 3:1–4)

What did Peter say to the man after the man had fixed his attention on Peter and John? What did Peter do to him and how did the man respond? How did the people respond to seeing this? (Acts 3:5–10)

What did Peter say to the crowd and what would be of benefit to them for heeding his message? (Acts 3:19–20)

Thursday

Read Acts 4

Why did the religious authorities have problems with the preaching of Peter and John and what did they do about it? (Acts 4:1–3)

How does Peter proclaim that salvation comes to mankind? (Acts 4:11–12)

Where did Peter and John go after being released and what specifically did they request in prayer? What happened after they prayed? (Acts 4:23–31)

Friday

Read Acts 5

Why did both Ananias and Sapphira die? (Acts 5:1–11)

Describe the atmosphere and happenings in and around the early Church as represented in Acts 5:12–16.

What does this story tell us about God's heart to have His message proclaimed? (Acts 5:17–21)

Read Acts 6

What problem cropped up in the church and how did the twelve solve it? What were the qualifications of those chosen to lead the ministry? (Acts 6:1–3)

Who was chosen for this ministry, what did the apostles do, and what were the results? (Acts 6:4–7)

Who was Stephen, what did God do through him, and what happened to him? (Acts 6:8–15)

Week 8 — This week's Bible reading continues our time in the book of Acts. We will look at Stephen before the Sanhedrin, the ministry of Philip, the conversion of Saul, Peter and Cornelius, the church at Antioch, and Peter's miraculous escape from prison.

Monday

Read Acts 7

What do we learn from this passage about Stephen's knowledge of Scripture? (Acts 7:2–8)

What did Stephen remind the Sanhedrin about concerning Moses? (Acts 7:20–29)

What did Stephen accuse the religious leaders of that made them furious to the point of killing him? (Acts 7:51–56)

Read Acts 8

Where did Philip go after the persecution broke out against the church in Jerusalem? What are we told about his ministry? (Acts 8:4–8)

What happened that caused Philip to meet the Ethiopian eunuch? (Acts 8:26–29)

What was the Ethiopian eunuch reading when Philip came to him? How did Philip respond to this opportunity to share the gospel? What were the results of this encounter? (Acts 8:30–39)

Read Acts 9

What was Saul's attitude toward believers as he set out for Damascus? What happened to him on the way? (Acts 9:1–9)

Summarize Ananias' interaction with the Lord over being sent to heal Saul. (Acts 9:10–16)

What did Saul do after he was healed and how did he escape from Damascus? (Acts 9:19–25)

Read Acts 10

Who was Cornelius and what do we learn about his habits? Who appeared to Cornelius and what did he tell him to do? (Acts 10:1–6)

How did God convince Peter to go with the Gentiles sent to him from Cornelius? (Acts 10:9–16, 19–20)

What happened to the gentiles who had gathered at Cornelius' home to hear Peter? How did Peter respond to this? (Acts 10:44–48)

Friday

Read Acts 11

How did the church at Antioch begin? What are we told about the hand of the Lord? (Acts 11:19–21)

When the church at Jerusalem heard about the Lord working at Antioch, who did they send? What are we told about this person? What are were told happened while he was there? (Acts 11:22–24)

What did Barnabas do next? What did he and Saul do at Antioch and for how long? (Acts 11:25–26)

55

Saturday

Read Acts 12

Why was Peter arrested? What did Herod intend to do to him? What are we told about the actions of the church given Peter's arrest? (Acts 12:1–5)

How did Peter escape from prison? (Acts 12:6–10)

Where did Peter go after escaping from prison? How did they respond to him? What did he share with them? (Acts 12:12–17)

Week 9 — This week's Bible reading continues our time in the book of Acts. We will look at Saul and Barnabas sent out, Paul's first missionary journey, the Council of Jerusalem, Paul's second missionary journey, and Paul at Berea, Athens, and Corinth.

Monday

Read Acts 13

How were Saul and Barnabas commissioned for their first missionary journey? Who sent them? (Acts 13:1–5)

Please explain what happened in Paphos. (Acts 13:6–12)

In Pisidian Antioch, where did Paul and Barnabas go to preach the gospel? What was the main thrust of Paul's preaching? (Acts 13:14, 38–39)

Tuesday

Read Acts 14

Where are we told that Paul and Barnabas preached in Iconium? What does this passage say about their effectiveness, God's hand at work, and their opposition? (Acts 14:1–7)

What caused the people of Lystra to try to sacrifice to Paul and Barnabas? (Acts 14:8–13)

What did Paul and Barnabas do as they revisited the churches that were planted? (Acts 14:21–23)

Read Acts 15

Why were Paul and Barnabas sent to Jerusalem by the church at Antioch? What did they do upon reaching Jerusalem? (Acts 15:1–4)

How did Peter defend the position of salvation through faith in Christ for the Gentiles? (Acts 15:7–11)

What did James conclude about the matter and what rules were given to Gentile believers? (Acts 15:19–21)

Read Acts 16

How was Lydia converted? Who was she and where did this occur? What does it say was the Lord's role? (Acts 16:11–15)

Why were Paul and Silas put into prison? (Acts 16:16–24)

Summarize what happened after Paul and Silas were imprisoned. (Acts 16:25–34)

Read Acts 17

What does this passage tell us about the Berean disciples? (Acts 17:10–12)

What was Paul's immediate response when he reached Athens? Where did he go to reason with those living there? (Acts. 17:16–17)

What did Paul preach to the Athenians about who God is and what He had done? (Acts 17:24–28)

Read Acts 18

What was Paul's normal practice when coming to a new location? (Acts 18:4,19)

How long did Paul stay in Corinth and what did he do during this time? (Acts 18:9–11)

Who was Apollos and why was he so helpful to the believers? (Acts 18:24–28)

Week 10 — This week's Bible reading continues our time in the book of Acts. We will look at Paul's ministry at Ephesus, the riot at Ephesus, the raising of Eutychus, the Ephesian farewell, and Paul at Jerusalem.

Monday

Read Acts 19:1–20

Who did Paul meet when he came to Ephesus? What do we learn about these disciples from this passage? (Acts 19:1–7)

Where did Paul go first to proclaim the kingdom of God? What did Paul do as result of the Way being maligned? How long are we told that Paul held daily lectures and what were the results of this ministry? (Acts 19:8–10)

What else are we told about Paul's ministry while at Ephesus? What happened as a result of the episode with the seven sons of Sceva? (Acts 19:11–20)

Tuesday

Read Acts 19:21–41

Who caused the disturbance at Ephesus and what were their reasons for opposition to the Way? (Acts 19:23–27)

What happened in the city as a result of the actions of the craftsmen? (Acts 19:28–34)

Who finally talked sense to the rioting crowd? What did this person say that broke the riot up? (Acts 19:35–41)

Read Acts 20

Why was Paul preaching at midnight? What happened to Eutychus that he fell from the window? How did Paul react to this accident? (Acts 20:7–12)

What do we learn about how Paul ministered when he was at Ephesus? (Acts 20:18–21)

How did Paul look at his own life? What else did Paul say about his life while among the Ephesians? (Acts 20:24, 33–35)

Read Acts 21

What did the prophet Agabus say that would happen to Paul at Jerusalem? How did those around Paul react to this? How did Paul respond? (Acts 21:10–14)

What did James and the elders at Jerusalem counsel Paul to do and why? What did Paul do in reaction to their advice? (Acts 21:20–26)

What were the circumstances surrounding Paul's arrest? (Acts 21:33–36)

Read Acts 22

What do we learn about Paul's past and his actions against the church from his discourse? (Acts 22:3–5)

What did Ananias tell Saul when he came and prayed for him? (Acts 22:12–16)

How did the crowd react to Paul telling them that he had been sent to the Gentiles? What did the Roman tribune order to be done to Paul? (Acts 22:21–24)

Read Acts 23

What did Paul say that caused a dispute to break out in the Sanhedrin? What do we learn about what the Sadducees and Pharisees believed? (Acts 23:6–8)

What happened the day after Paul spoke to the Sanhedrin? How was this plot against Paul to be carried out? (Acts 23:12–15)

How did Paul escape from this plot to take his life? What did the Roman commander do after hearing about the plot? (Acts 23:16–24)

Week 11 — This week's Bible reading concludes our time in the book of Acts. We will look at Paul standing trial before Felix, before Festus, and before Agrippa. We'll also look at Paul and the shipwreck, Paul on Malta, and Paul arriving at Rome.

Monday

Read Acts 24

What accusations were brought against Paul? What was Paul's initial defense against these accusations? (Acts 24:5–6, 11–13)

What else did Paul testify about concerning his own life? (Acts 24:14–16)

How did Felix treat Paul after his testimony? What did Felix ultimately do with Paul? (Acts 24:23–27)

Tuesday

Read Acts 25

What are we told about the accusations brought against Paul? How did Paul react to these accusations? (Acts 25:7–8)

How did Paul respond to Festus' idea of trying him in Jerusalem? (Acts 25:9–12)

How did Festus describe Paul's situation and recent events to King Agrippa? (Acts 25:18–21)

Wednesday

Read Acts 26:1–18

What information is provided in this passage concerning Paul's heritage as a Jew? What did Paul provide as the reason he was on trial? What question did he raise at the end of this passage? (Acts 26:4–8)

What else did Paul say that emphasized his zeal in persecuting Christians? (Acts 26:9–11)

Summarize what Jesus told Paul on the Damascus Road encounter. What specifically did Jesus call Paul to do? (Acts 26:15–18)

Read Acts 26:19–32

What did Paul share with King Agrippa that he did in response to the vision? What message did he preach? (Acts 26:19–20)

What did Paul preach that Moses and the prophets said would happen? (Acts 26:22–23)

How did Paul attempt to persuade King Agrippa? How did Agrippa respond? What was Paul's desire for those who were listening to his testimony? (Acts 26:26–29)

..

Friday

Read Acts 27

What did Paul say to warn the men in charge of the ship? How did the centurion react to Paul's warning? What do we learn about how the decision was made to continue sailing? (Acts 27:9–12)

What do we learn about the condition of Paul and the men on the ship at this point? What did Paul tell the men on board about what would happen to them? (Acts 27:20–26)

How else did Paul encourage the men on board? What did Paul do in front of them all? What effect did this have? (Acts 27:33–37)

Read Acts 28

What happened to Paul once ashore on Malta? How did the islanders react to Paul being bitten by the snake? (Acts 28:3–6)

What happened at Publius' estate? What effect did this have on the islanders of Malta and Paul's journey onward to Rome? (Acts 28:7–10)

What did Paul do to try and convince the Jews at Rome about Jesus? How did they react to Paul's preaching? What else do we learn about Paul's time while in Rome? (Acts 28:23–24, 30–31)

Week 12 — This week's Bible reading will bring us to the books of 1 John and 2 Peter. We will look at Jesus as our Advocate, our new identity in Christ, God's definition of love, confidence in eternity, false teachers, and end times.

Monday

Read 1 John 1–2

Why did the Apostle John write this letter? Who speaks to the Father in our defense? (1 John 2:1–2)

What does this passage say about those who claim to be without sin? What does God promise us? (1 John 1:8–10)

What is told to us about those who love the world and the one who does the will of God? (1 John 2:15–17)

Tuesday

Read 1 John 3

What is our new identity in Christ? What are we told about what we will become? (1 John 3:1–3)

What is the message we have heard from the beginning? About what should we not be surprised? How can we have confidence in our eternal destiny? (1 John 3:11–15)

What do we learn about love from these verses? What is the command we have received? (1 John 3:16–18, 23)

Wednesday

Read 1 John 4

How are we told that God made His love manifest among us? How are we to respond to this? (1 John 4:9–11)

What evidence do we have that God lives in us? What are we told about those who confess Jesus as God's Son? (1 John 4:13–15)

Summarize what these verses are telling us. (1 John 4:19–21)

Thursday

Read 1 John 5

How is love for God defined? What is said about those who overcome the world? (1 John 5:3–5)

What do these verses say about those who have eternal life? (1 John 5:11–12)

Why did John write these things? What things did John affirm as things he knew? (1 John 5:13, 18–20)

Read 2 Peter 1–2

What characteristics of false teachers are described in these verses? (2 Peter 2:1–3, 10–12)

How do these verses say we can escape the corruption in the world? How are we told that God imparted the prophecy of Scripture to mankind? (2 Peter 1:3–4, 20–21)

What other attributes are given to us to identify false teachers? (2 Peter 2:17–19)

Read 2 Peter 3

What was Peter asking the reader to remember? (2 Peter 3:2)

What do these verses say about scoffers and what they deliberately overlook? (2 Peter 3:3–5)

How will the present earth be destroyed? What is our hope when facing this? (2 Peter 3:7, 10–13)

Week 13 — In this week's Bible reading we will study the book of James and Psalm 49. In James, we will be looking at being doers of the word, faith and deeds, the tongue, prayer, and warnings to the rich. In Psalm 49, we will look at the wise, foolish, and the wealthy.

Monday

Read James 1

What are we told about asking God for wisdom and the conditions necessary to receive? (James 1:5–8)

What do we learn about temptation from these verses? List the sequence of events that lead to death. (James 1:13–15)

What is the danger in listening to the word without accompanying actions? What analogy is used to depict this? How are we told we can be blessed in what we do? (James 1:22–25)

Tuesday

Read James 2

What warning are we given here? What example is given to illustrate this issue? (James 2:1–4)

What do we learn about the poor and the rich? (James 2:5–7)

What examples are given in these verses to demonstrate that faith and actions must work together for faith to be complete? (James 2:20–26)

Wednesday

Read James 3

What analogies were used for the tongue in these verses? What else are we told about the tongue? (James 3:3–6)

What are we told about man's ability to tame the tongue? What is compared here to fresh water and salt water? (James 3:7–12)

How is wisdom that comes from heaven described? (James 3:17)

Read James 4

What reason is given why our prayers are not answered? (James 4:1–3)

List the things we are encouraged to do and the corresponding things that will happen if we do them? (James 4:7–10)

What example of boasting is given here? How is our temporary life depicted? How is sin defined in verse 17? (James 4:13–17)

Friday

Read James 5

What warnings are given to those who are rich in this present age? (James 5:1–6)

What are we encouraged to do in these verses? What are we warned against as we do this? (James 5:7–9)

What instructions are given to those who are in suffering, cheerful or sick? What else do we learn about prayer? (James 5:13–18)

Read Psalm 49

What does the Psalmist say concerning the wise, the fool, and the stupid? What is said about the path of those who have foolish confidence? (Psalm 49:10–14)

What does the Psalmist speak concerning his own salvation? (Psalm 49:15)

What wisdom does the Psalmist provide to help bring perspective to wealth? (Psalm 49:16–20)

Weekly Memory Verses

Week 1 — Luke 1:37 — "For nothing will be impossible with God." (ESV)

Week 2 — Luke 6:38 — "give, and it will be given to you. Good measure, pressed down, shaken together, running over, will be put into your lap. For with the measure you use it will be measured back to you." (ESV)

Week 3 — Luke 12:31 — "Instead, seek his kingdom, and these things will be added to you." (ESV)

Week 4 — Luke 16:10 — "One who is faithful in a very little is also faithful in much, and one who is dishonest in a very little is also dishonest in much." (ESV)

Week 5 — Luke 19:10 — "For the Son of Man came to seek and to save the lost." (ESV)

Week 6 — Luke 24:46–47 — "Thus is what is written, that the Christ should suffer and on the third day rise from the dead, and that repentance for the forgiveness of sins should be proclaimed in his name to all nations, beginning from Jerusalem." (ESV)

Week 7 — Acts 1:8 — "But you will receive power when the Holy Spirit has come upon you, and you will be my witnesses in Jerusalem and in all Judea and Samaria, and to the end of the earth." (ESV)

Week 8 — Acts 10:34–35 — "So Peter opened his mouth and said: 'Truly I understand that God shows no partiality, but in every nation anyone who fears him and does what is right is acceptable to him.'" (ESV)

Week 9 — Acts 13:39 — "and by him everyone who believes is freed from everything from which you could not be freed by the law of Moses." (ESV)

Week 10 — Acts 20:21 — "testifying both to Jews and to Greeks of repentance toward God and of faith in our Lord Jesus Christ." (ESV)

Week 11 — Acts 28:31 — "proclaiming the kingdom of God and teaching about the Lord Jesus Christ with all boldness and without hindrance." (ESV)

Week 12 — 1 John 4:7 — "Beloved, let us love one another, for love is from God, and whoever loves has been born of God and knows God." (ESV)

Week 13 — James 1:2–4 — "Count it all joy, my brothers, when you meet trials of various kinds, for you know that the testing of your faith produces steadfastness. And let steadfastness have its full effect, that you may be perfect and complete, lacking in nothing." (ESV)

Journal & Notes

Journal & Notes

Journal & Notes

Journal & Notes

Journal & Notes

Journal & Notes

Journal & Notes

Journal & Notes

Journal & Notes

Journal & Notes

Journal & Notes

Journal & Notes

Journal & Notes

Made in the USA
Las Vegas, NV
06 November 2023

80353684R00057